Specific Skill Series

Following Directions

Richard A. Boning

Fifth Edition

SRA/McGraw-Hill

Columbus, Ohio

Cover, Back Cover, ZEFA/Germany/The Stock Market

SRA/McGraw-Hill

A Division of The McGraw·Hill Companies

Printed in the United States of America.

Send all inquiries to:
   SRA/McGraw-Hill
   8787 Orion Place
   Columbus, OH 43240-4027

ISBN 0-02-687932-8

      6 7 8 IPC 02 01 00

To the Teacher

PURPOSE:
FOLLOWING DIRECTIONS is designed to develop skill in reading, understanding, and following instructions and directions. Proficiency in this basic skill is essential for success in every school subject and in nonacademic activities as well.

FOR WHOM:
The skill of FOLLOWING DIRECTIONS is developed through a series of books spanning ten levels (Picture, Preparatory, A, B, C, D, E, F, G, H). The Picture Level is for pupils who have not acquired a basic sight vocabulary. The Preparatory Level is for pupils who have a basic sight vocabulary but are not yet ready for the first-grade-level book. Books A through H are appropriate for pupils who can read on levels one through eight, respectively. **The use of the *Specific Skill Series Placement Test* is recommended to determine the appropriate level.**

THE NEW EDITION:
The fifth edition of the *Specific Skill Series* maintains the quality and focus that has distinguished this program for more than 25 years. A key element central to the program's success has been the unique nature of the reading selections. Nonfiction pieces about current topics have been designed to stimulate the interest of students, motivating them to use the comprehension strategies they have learned to further their reading. To keep this important aspect of the program intact, a percentage of the reading selections have been replaced in order to ensure the continued relevance of the subject material.

In addition, a significant percentage of the artwork in the program has been replaced to give the books a contemporary look. The cover photographs are designed to appeal to readers of all ages.

SESSIONS:
Short practice sessions are the most effective. It is desirable to have a practice session every day or every other day, using a few units each session.

SCORING:
Pupils should record their answers on the reproducible worksheets. The worksheets make scoring easier and provide uniform records of the pupils' work. Using work-sheets also avoids consuming the exercise books.

To the Teacher

It is important for pupils to know how well they are doing. For this reason, units should be scored as soon as they have been completed. Then a discussion can be held in which pupils justify their choices. (The Integrated Language Activities, many of which are open-ended, do not lend themselves to an objective score; thus there are no answer keys for these pages.)

GENERAL INFORMATION ON *FOLLOWING DIRECTIONS*:

FOLLOWING DIRECTIONS focuses attention on four types of directions. The *testing and drilling* directions are like those in most textbooks and workbooks. Mastery of this type, so vital to school success, is stressed throughout FOLLOWING DIRECTIONS. The second type of direction is found in science books and involves *experimenting*. Such material requires the reader to find an answer to a problem or provides the reader with an example of practical application of a principle.

The third type of direction, *assembling*, deals with parts or ingredients and the order and way in which they are put together. Here the purpose is to make or create, rather than to solve a problem or demonstrate a principle.

Directions which tell how to do something are *performing* directions. They accent the steps in learning to do something new. The focus is on the performance rather than on the product.

SUGGESTED STEPS:

On levels A-H, pupils read the information above the first line. Then they answer the questions *below* this line. (Pupils are *not* to respond in writing to information *above* the first line; they are only to study it. Pupils should not write or mark anything in this book.) On the Picture Level, pupils tell if a picture correctly follows the directions. On the Preparatory Level, pupils tell which picture out of two correctly follows the directions.

Additional information on using FOLLOWING DIRECTIONS with pupils will be found in the **Specific Skill Series Teacher's Manual**.

RELATED MATERIALS:

Specific Skill Series Placement Tests, which enable the teacher to place pupils at their appropriate levels in each skill, are available for the Elementary (Pre-1–6) and Midway (4–8) grade levels.

About This Book

Following directions is an important part of your life. At home, your parents may say, "Wash your hands before you eat." In school, your teacher may say, "Write your name at the top of your paper." On the street, the crossing guard may say, "Do not cross yet."

Following directions is like trying to find your way with a map. If you follow the map correctly, you will get where you want to go. If you make a mistake, you will get lost.

It is important to understand directions. It is important to follow them correctly.

Reading directions is different from reading a story. Directions should be read carefully. Ask yourself questions like these: What do the directions tell me to do? Do I understand all the words in the directions? Should I do one thing before I do another?

In this book, you will read different kinds of directions. Some directions are the kind you see on tests and in workbooks. Some directions tell how to find out facts about something. Some directions tell how to do things, such as play a game. You do not have to follow the directions.

Instead, you will finish sentences and answer questions about each set of directions. First you will choose two answers that tell what the directions say to do. Then you will see how someone followed the directions. Think about the directions. Think about how they were followed. Then answer the question, "Is it right?" Choose **Yes** if the directions were followed correctly. Choose **No** if the directions were not followed correctly.

DIRECTIONS:

Put an X on the picture that shows what we cook on.

---

1. You are looking for something to—
    (A) **sleep in**
    (B) **ride on**
    (C) **cook on**

---

2. The answer must have—
    (A) **an X on it**
    (B) **a line under it**
    (C) **a circle around it**

---

3. Is it right? (A) **Yes** (B) **No**

UNIT 2

DIRECTIONS:

Look at the signs. Draw circles around the two signs that are the same.

1. You are asked to find two signs that are—
   - **(A) different**
   - **(B) the same**
   - **(C) almost the same**

2. You are asked to draw—
   - **(A) circles**
   - **(B) faces**
   - **(C) lines**

3. Is it right?   **(A) Yes**   **(B) No**

DIRECTIONS:

Draw a line from the goat to the horse. Put a circle around the pig.

1. You are to find—

    (A) one animal
    (B) two animals
    (C) three animals

2. You are to make—

    (A) a line and a circle
    (B) an X and a line
    (C) two lines

3. Is it right?   **(A)** Yes   **(B)** No

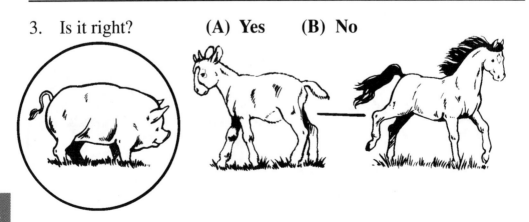

DIRECTIONS:

Find the picture of the basket. Put an X on it. Put a line under the picture of the tree.

1. You are to find the—

    (A) tree and basket

    (B) clock and tree

    (C) tree

2. You are asked to make—

    (A) an X and a line

    (B) a circle and an X

    (C) a check and an X

3. Is this right?   **(A) Yes**   **(B) No**

UNIT 5

DIRECTIONS:

Find the boy with the cup and the girl with the bell. Draw a line under each.

1. You are asked to find—

      (A) two boys
      (B) a boy and a girl
      (C) two girls

2. You are asked to make—

      (A) one line
      (B) two lines
      (C) one X

3. Is this right?   **(A) Yes**   **(B) No**

DIRECTIONS:

Put an X under the picture that does not belong with the others.

---

1. You are to find the picture that—
   - **(A) does not belong**
   - **(B) belongs**
   - **(C) is prettiest**

2. You are to make—
   - **(A) an X**
   - **(B) a circle**
   - **(C) a line**

3. Is it right?   **(A) Yes   (B) No**

DIRECTIONS:

Put a circle around the picture of something good to eat. Put a line under the thing that makes noise.

1. You are asked to look for—

    (A) one thing
    (B) two things
    (C) a star

2. You must make a circle and—

    (A) a line
    (B) an X
    (C) a picture

3. Is it right?   **(A) Yes**   **(B) No**

DIRECTIONS:

Draw a line from the dog to the kitten that is crying.

1. You are asked to find the kitten that is crying and the—
   (A) **dog**
   (B) **girl**
   (C) **duck**

2. The right pictures must have a line—
   (A) **over them**
   (B) **on them**
   (C) **between them**

3. Is it right?   (A) **Yes**   (B) **No**

DIRECTIONS:

Find the picture of the girl reading. Put a check mark under it.

1. You are to find the girl who is—

   (A) looking
   (B) reading
   (C) showing

2. Your answer should be—

   (A) a check
   (B) a circle
   (C) a line

3. Is it right?   **(A) Yes**   **(B) No**

DIRECTIONS:

Put a line under the word that tells what the picture is.

neck   eyes

mouth   nose

---

1. You are to look for the—
   - (A) **right word**
   - (B) **eyes**
   - (C) **neck**

---

2. The answer must have a line—
   - (A) **on it**
   - (B) **under it**
   - (C) **over it**

---

3. Is it right?   (A) **Yes**   (B) **No**

<u>neck</u>   eyes

mouth   nose

DIRECTIONS:

Draw lines from the pictures to the right words.

girl

carrot

train

fork

boy

chair

---

1. You are to find the right words to go with the—
    - **(A) pictures**
    - **(B) sentences**
    - **(C) circles**

---

2. You are to—
    - **(A) cross out words**
    - **(B) draw lines**
    - **(C) underline words**

---

3. Is it right?   **(A) Yes**   **(B) No**

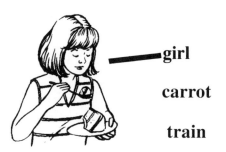

girl

carrot

train

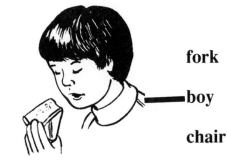

fork

boy

chair

DIRECTIONS:

Circle the word that tells the thing the boy is banging.

drum   girl

doll   boy

bike   airplane

---

1. You are to find the word that tells about—
    - **(A) the house**
    - **(B) the picture**
    - **(C) your friend**

---

2. The word should be—
    - **(A) circled**
    - **(B) checked**
    - **(C) underlined**

---

3. Is it right?   **(A) Yes**   **(B) No**

drum   girl

doll   boy

bike   airplane

A. Exercising Your Skill

A **direction** tells you how to make or do something. Directions give you steps to follow. In good directions, the steps are in the right order.

These directions tell you how to make a peanut butter sandwich. The directions are not in the right order. On your paper, write the steps in the right order.

Open the jar of peanut butter.
Get two slices of bread, a jar of peanut butter, and a knife.
Put the two slices of bread together.
Use the knife to spread peanut butter on one slice of bread.
Eat your sandwich.

B. Expanding Your Skill

Talk about the directions in Part A with your classmates. Answer these questions:

- What do you need?
- What do you do first?
- What else do you do?
- How do you finish?
- What would happen if you did not follow the steps in the right order?

C. Exploring Language

The things listed below can be used to make a sandwich. You would probably not use all of them in the same sandwich, though! Read the list of things. Pick some that you think would go well together in a sandwich. Then write directions that tell how to make the sandwich. Some words you may need to use in your directions are slice, chop, mix, and spread.

ham	brown bread	apples
egg	white bread	tuna fish
cheese	toast	butter
chicken	peanut butter	jam

D. Expressing Yourself

Do one of these things.

1. Draw pictures to go with the sandwich directions you wrote. Your pictures should show each step in making the sandwich.

2. Find out how to spell the names of some of your favorite foods. Make your own food word book. Next to each word, draw a picture of the food.

3. Find directions for a snack you could make at school. Work with others from your class to write the directions on big paper. Get the things you will need. Then work together with others to make a snack for your class.

DIRECTIONS:

Look at this picture. Something is not there. Think what it is. Draw it.

1. You are to look for something that is—
   (A) **not there**
   (B) **there**
   (C) **in school**

2. When you think of what is not there, you are to—
   (A) **draw it**
   (B) **circle it**
   (C) **color it**

3. Is it right? (A) **Yes** (B) **No**

UNIT 14

DIRECTIONS:

Draw lines from the pictures to the right words.

monkey

ring

horse

squirrel

dragon

tree

---

1. You are asked to find the pictures and—
   - (A) big houses
   - (B) right words
   - (C) schools

---

2. You are to—
   - (A) draw lines
   - (B) circle the pictures
   - (C) circle the words

---

3. Is it right?   (A) Yes   (B) No

monkey

ring

horse

squirrel

dragon

tree

DIRECTIONS:

Put a ring around the sentence that tells about the picture.

The boy walks.

The girl sings.

The boy runs fast.

---

1. You are to look for a sentence that goes with the—
      (A) ring
      (B) girl
      (C) picture

---

2. Around your answer you must have a—
      (A) number
      (B) ring
      (C) color

---

3. Is it right?   **(A) Yes**   **(B) No**

The boy walks.

The girl sings.

The boy runs fast.

DIRECTIONS:

These letters are mixed up. Put them in the right order, numbering them 1, 2, 3, 4, 5. They will then spell the name of a fruit.

palep

p _____
a _____
l _____
e _____
p _____

---

1. You are asked to find the name of a—
    (A) fruit
    (B) rock
    (C) shoe

---

2. Your answer should be shown with—
    (A) letters
    (B) words
    (C) numbers

---

3. Is it right?   (A) Yes   (B) No

palep

p _2_
a _1_
l _4_
e _5_
p _3_

DIRECTIONS:

Put a line under the words that tell what a baby can do.

read a book

play baseball

sleep and cry

---

1. You are to look for things that a baby—
   (A) **can do**
   (B) **cannot do**
   (C) **likes to eat**

---

2. You are to make a—
   (A) **line**
   (B) **circle**
   (C) **letter**

---

3. Is it right?　　(A) **Yes**　　(B) **No**

read a book

play baseball

sleep and cry

DIRECTIONS:

Write **Yes** or **No** after each sentence.

Animals read books. _____

A mouse is small. _____

Snow is warm. _____

---

1. You are asked to—
   - (A) number
   - (B) color
   - (C) write

2. Your answer must have—
   - (A) an X
   - (B) Yes or No
   - (C) a circle

3. Is it right?　　　(A) Yes　　(B) No

Animals read books. ___✗_____

A mouse is small. ___✗_____

Snow is warm. ___✗_____

DIRECTIONS:

Find the picture of a house with a garden around it. Put a line under it.

1. You are asked to find the—

   (A) stores
   (B) house and garden
   (C) school

2. Your answer must have a—

   (A) check mark
   (B) line under it
   (C) circle around it

3. Is it right?   (A) Yes   (B) No

DIRECTIONS:

Cross out the two words that do not complete the sentence.

	air.
Trains run on	**water.**
	tracks.

---

1. You are to look for two words that do not—
   - (A) end with "t"
   - (B) rhyme
   - (C) complete the sentence

2. The words must be—
   - (A) crossed out
   - (B) underlined
   - (C) circled

3. Is it right?   (A) Yes   (B) No

	air.
Trains run on	**water.**
	tracks.

DIRECTIONS:

Draw a line under the two words that do not begin the sentence.

Fish

Monkeys   **eat bananas.**

Flowers

---

1. You are to look for two words that do not—
   - **(A) begin the sentence**
   - **(B) complete the sentence**
   - **(C) rhyme**

---

2. The words should be—
   - **(A) underlined**
   - **(B) crossed out**
   - **(C) circled**

---

3. Is it right?   **(A) Yes**   **(B) No**

Fish

Monkeys   **eat bananas.**

Flowers

DIRECTIONS:

Do things weigh less under water? Here is how you can find out.

EXPERIMENT

Fill a big can with water. Hold a rock in your hand. See how heavy it is. Now put the rock into the water. Does the rock still feel as heavy?

---

1. You are asked to find out if things weigh less—
    - **(A) under water**
    - **(B) under a rock**
    - **(C) in a little can**

---

2. You are asked to put water in—
    - **(A) a rock**
    - **(B) a big can**
    - **(C) your hand**

---

3. You are to place the rock—
    - **(A) into the water**
    - **(B) under the can**
    - **(C) under the ground**

DIRECTIONS:

Draw a circle around the picture of a man working by a truck.

1. You are asked to find the man—
    - **(A) working**
    - **(B) singing**
    - **(C) playing**

2. Your answer must have—
    - **(A) a line under it**
    - **(B) a circle around it**
    - **(C) an X on it**

3. Is it right?   **(A) Yes   (B) No**

DIRECTIONS:

The letters in the word below are mixed up. The word means "not happy." Write the letters in order on the line.

d s a

_____

---

1. You are to write the letters—
       (A) **mixed up**
       (B) **in order**
       (C) **the same way**

---

2. Your answer should be on the—
       (A) **line**
       (B) **board**
       (C) **picture**

---

3. Is it right?   (A) **Yes**   (B) **No**

_____ sad _____

A. Exercising Your Skill

Directions may tell you how to mark an answer. These are some directions you may read:

put an X on	draw a line under
circle	put a check mark next to
draw a ring around	write **T** for <u>true</u>

Read each set of directions below. See how the answers were marked. On your paper, number 1 to 6. After each number, write **yes** if the answer is correctly marked. Write **no** if the answer is not correctly marked.

1. Draw a line under the word. ~~monkeys~~

2. Put an X on the word. ~~school~~

3. Draw a ring around the word. Monday ✓

4. Put a check mark after the sentence below.
   Trains run on tracks. ✓

5. Circle the word. <u>water</u>

6. Write **T** for <u>true</u> and **F** for <u>false</u>.
   Fish live in water. _T_

B. Expanding Your Skill

Look through workbooks and other books. On your paper, write two sets of directions that are used. Talk about the sets of directions with others in your class. Talk about how the directions are different. Answer these questions:

- What do the directions tell me to do?
- How should I mark my answers?

C. Exploring Language

The set of directions below is not complete. Copy the directions onto your paper. Add a word for each blank. Use some of the direction words from Part A and Part B.

First, get a piece of paper. At the top of the paper, draw a _____. Under the _____, draw a _____. Then _____ the _____. At the bottom of the paper, draw a _____.

Trade papers with a classmate. Follow the directions your classmate wrote.

D. Expressing Yourself

Do one of these things.

1. Think about the rules you have learned for following directions. Work with your class to make a chart called "Following Directions." List the rules to follow. List them in the right order.

2. Pick a set of directions. These can be from a workbook, a game, or any other place. Read the directions. Then write a list of questions about the directions. Trade directions and questions with someone else. Answer each other's questions.

3. Work with a partner. Take turns giving each other directions. You can give directions for sharpening a pencil, drawing a picture, or anything you choose. Try to follow the directions correctly, step by step.

DIRECTIONS:

Do heavy things fall faster than light things? Here is how you can find out.

EXPERIMENT

Hold a penny in one hand. In the other hand hold a brick. Let both fall at the same time. Does the brick hit the ground before the penny does?

1. You are to find out if heavy things fall—
   - **(A) easier**
   - **(B) higher**
   - **(C) faster**

2. You are asked to hold a brick in one hand. In the other hand hold a—
   - **(A) can**
   - **(B) stone**
   - **(C) penny**

3. You are asked to see which falls—
   - **(A) down**
   - **(B) faster**
   - **(C) up**

DIRECTIONS:

Say each word. Find the one that does not belong with the others. Put a check mark after it.

car _____

bus _____

oven _____

bike _____

---

1. You are to look for the word that—
   - (A) **does not belong**
   - (B) **starts like bus**
   - (C) **is very funny**

2. You are asked to make a—
   - (A) **check mark**
   - (B) **circle**
   - (C) **X**

3. Is it right?   (A) **Yes**   (B) **No**

car _____

bus _____

oven ✔

bike _____

DIRECTIONS:

Find the picture of something you must put on a letter before you mail it. Underline the picture.

1. You are asked to find something to put on a—

      (A) letter
      (B) dog
      (C) turtle

2. Your answer must be—

      (A) circled
      (B) checked
      (C) underlined

3. Is it right?   **(A) Yes**   **(B) No**

DIRECTIONS:

Find the word that does not belong. Place a check mark after it.

penny

nickel

dime

dollar

---

1. You are to look for the different—
    - **(A) word**
    - **(B) sentence**
    - **(C) letter**

2. To show the answer you are to make a—
    - **(A) circle**
    - **(B) check mark**
    - **(C) line**

3. Is it right?   **(A) Yes**   **(B) No**

penny

nickel

dime

dollar

DIRECTIONS:

Draw a ring around the words that go with the picture.

The fish are jumping.

A birthday party is fun.

The stars are bright.

---

1. You are to look for words that—

   (A) go with the picture
   (B) are very funny
   (C) rhyme with fun

---

2. The answer should have a—

   (A) ring around it
   (B) line under it
   (C) X on it

---

3. Is it right?   **(A) Yes   (B) No**

The fish are jumping.

A birthday party is fun.

The stars are bright.

DIRECTIONS:

Draw a line from the picture to the right sentence.

The man builds a house.

The man falls off the ladder.

The man cleans the house.

---

1. You are asked to look for the right—
   - **(A) sentence**
   - **(B) school**
   - **(C) house**

---

2. There must be a line from the sentence to the right—
   - **(A) animal**
   - **(B) picture**
   - **(C) people**

---

3. Is it right?   **(A) Yes**   **(B) No**

The man builds a house.

The man falls off the ladder.

The man cleans the house.

DIRECTIONS:

In each word there are two little words. Draw a ring around each of the two small words that make up the big words.

doorbell

airplane

something

---

1. You are to look for the—
      (A) little words
      (B) sentence
      (C) pictures

2. You are to draw rings around—
      (A) one big word
      (B) one small word
      (C) each small word

3. Is it right?   **(A)** Yes   **(B)** No

DIRECTIONS:

Draw a line from the picture to the right sentence.

The children are watching TV.

The children are swimming in the pool.

The children are reading.

---

1. You are to find the sentence that tells about the—
    - **(A) picture**
    - **(B) word**
    - **(C) letter**

---

2. You are to draw a—
    - **(A) picture**
    - **(B) line**
    - **(C) slide**

---

3. Is it right?   **(A) Yes**   **(B) No**

The children are watching TV.

The children are swimming in the pool.

The children are reading.

DIRECTIONS:

To make new words, add the letter **s** to the end of the words below.

run _____

walk _____

jump _____

---

1. You are asked to add the—
    - **(A) letter s**
    - **(B) letter c**
    - **(C) numbers**

---

2. Your answers are to be placed at the—
    - **(A) start**
    - **(B) end**
    - **(C) top**

---

3. Is it right?   **(A) Yes**   **(B) No**

runs_____

walks_____

jumps_____

DIRECTIONS:

Find the picture of the person who brings us letters. Put an X on this picture.

---

1. You are asked to find the—

    (A) **mail person**

    (B) **wood**

    (C) **police officer**

---

2. You are told to make—

    (A) **an X**

    (B) **a circle**

    (C) **a line**

---

3. Is it right?   (A) **Yes**   (B) **No**

DIRECTIONS:

Write **T** after every sentence that is true or right. Write **F** after every sentence that is false or wrong.

Elephants climb trees.＿＿＿＿＿＿＿＿＿＿

Cats like fish. ＿＿＿＿＿＿＿＿＿＿＿＿＿

Horses can fly.＿＿＿＿＿＿＿＿＿＿＿＿

---

1. You are to find sentences that are—

      (A) True
      (B) False
      (C) True or False

---

2. After each sentence write—

      (A) F
      (B) T
      (C) T or F

---

3. Is it right?   **(A) Yes**   **(B) No**

Elephants climb trees.＿＿＿T＿＿＿＿＿

Cats like fish.＿＿＿＿F＿＿＿＿＿

Horses can fly.＿＿＿＿F＿＿＿＿＿

DIRECTIONS:

Find the picture of the woman looking out of the window. Circle it.

1. You are told to find the woman looking—

          (A) at a book

          (B) at the window

          (C) out of the window

2. You are asked to show the answer with—

          (A) an X

          (B) a check

          (C) a circle

3. Is it right?   **(A) Yes**   **(B) No**

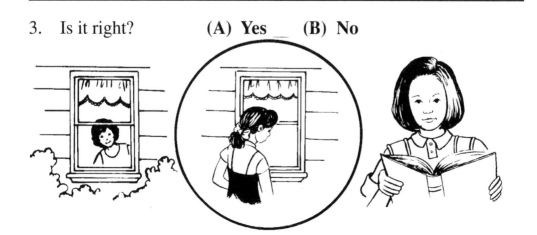

DIRECTIONS:

Put a check mark after the sentence that goes with the picture.

People are riding on the bus.

School is about to begin.

The children are going home.

---

1. You are to look for words that tell about the—
      (A) **picture**
      (B) **bus**
      (C) **dog**

---

2. You are to show the answer by making a check mark—
      (A) **before it**
      (B) **after it**
      (C) **under it**

---

3. Is it right?   (A) **Yes**   (B) **No**

People are riding on the bus.

School is about to begin.

The children are going home.

DIRECTIONS:

One person says two words. The other children try to think if the words rhyme. If the words rhyme, the children say **Yes**. If the words do not rhyme, the children say **No**.

---

1. This is a game of—

      (A) **rhyming**

      (B) **singing**

      (C) **running**

---

2. If the words rhyme, the other children say—

      (A) **Hello**

      (B) **Yes**

      (C) **No**

---

3. If the words do not rhyme, the others say—

      (A) **Yes**

      (B) **No**

      (C) **Good-by**

The Third L A P
Language Activity Pages

A. Exercising Your Skill

Directions give you steps to follow. The steps may be numbered, or they may use words like <u>first</u>, <u>next</u>, and <u>then</u>. Follow the steps in order.

These directions tell you how to create a special code to write secret messages.

TWO BLANKS

First, draw a chart with nine boxes across and six boxes down. Next, write the letters of the alphabet, like this.

A	B	C	D	E	F	G	H	I
J	K	L	M	N	O	P	Q	R
S	T	U	V	W	X	Y	Z	

Then, write a number in the box below each letter. If you mix up the numbers, the code will not be too easy. Look at this chart.

A	B	C	D	E	F	G	H	I
7	9	11	8	10	12	1	3	5
J	K	L	M	N	O	P	Q	R
2	4	6	13	15	17	18	14	16
S	T	U	V	W	X	Y	Z	
19	21	23	20	22	24	25	26	

To spell a word in code, first find each letter in the chart. Then write the number that is below each letter. Put dots between numbers in a word.

Now use the Two Blanks Code to solve this message.

1st word — 21 • 22 • 17   2nd word — 9 • 6 • 7 • 15 • 4 • 19
3rd word — 11 • 17 • 8 • 10

B. Expanding Your Skill

What words in the directions helped you know the order to follow? On your paper, list the words that tell the order of the steps needed to make a Two Blanks Code.

C. Exploring Language

Read carefully the directions for the Two Blanks Code in Part A. Then figure out what this message means. Write the message on your paper.

11 • 17 • 8 • 10 • 19   7 • 16 • 10   12 • 23 • 15

Next, use the code to write your own secret message. Trade messages with a friend. Now try to figure out what your friend's message is.

D. Expressing Yourself

Do one of these things.

1. Make up a code of your own. Write a set of directions for using the code. Explain the directions to a friend so that you can trade secret messages.

2. Draw a simple picture. Do not show it to anybody. Give directions to one or more people. Tell them how to draw the very same thing. After they have followed your directions, look at all the pictures. Do they look the same as your picture?

DIRECTIONS:

Read the two words in each line. Write another word of the same kind at the end of the line.

cow	dog	_____
red	green	_____
train	boat	_____

---

1. You are to think of words that are—
   (A) the same kind
   (B) not the same kind
   (C) spelled the same way

2. Your answer is to be—
   (A) written
   (B) numbered
   (C) circled

3. Is it right?   (A) Yes   (B) No

cow	dog	_pig_
red	green	_blue_
train	boat	_car_

UNIT 40

DIRECTIONS:

Here is how to play Mystery Tune. One person hums a song. The others listen. Then they try to guess the name of the song. The first one who guesses will get to hum the next song.

1. This shows you how to play—
        (A) **Mystery Story**
        (B) **Mystery Tune**
        (C) **Missing Tune**

2. Everyone tries to guess the name of the—
        (A) **singer**
        (B) **child**
        (C) **song**

3. The person who guesses will get to hum—
        (A) **the same song**
        (B) **a new song**
        (C) **a scale**

DIRECTIONS:

In each line one word does not end like the other words. Find that word. Put a line under it.

hen	cat	fat
red	ate	bed
car	far	sit

---

1. You are to look at the—
   - (A) **first letters**
   - (B) **ends of words**
   - (C) **pictures**

---

2. On each line one word should be—
   - (A) **circled**
   - (B) **underlined**
   - (C) **checked**

---

3. Is it right? (A) **Yes** (B) **No**

<u>hen</u>	cat	fat
red	<u>ate</u>	bed
car	far	<u>sit</u>

UNIT 42

DIRECTIONS:

Which word would you put in the blank? Circle the word you choose.

Cats ——————— mice.   catch

train

drink

---

1. You are to look for the word that is—
    - (A) missing
    - (B) hidden
    - (C) spoken

2. When you find it, you are to—
    - (A) check it
    - (B) circle it
    - (C) underline it

3. Is it right?   (A) Yes   (B) No

Cats ——————— mice.   catch

train

drink

53

DIRECTIONS:

Here is how you can find out what will happen to water that is left in a glass.

EXPERIMENT

Take a glass of water. Make sure the glass is filled to the very top. Do not touch it again. Look at it in seven days. See what has happened.

---

1. You are to find out what happens to water when it is—
    - (A) **not touched**
    - (B) **touched**
    - (C) **used**

---

2. You are asked to fill the glass—
    - (A) **to the top**
    - (B) **half way**
    - (C) **with milk**

---

3. You are to look at the glass in—
    - (A) **two days**
    - (B) **one day**
    - (C) **seven days**

DIRECTIONS:

Why is salt put on icy streets? Here is how you can find out.

EXPERIMENT

Get two ice cubes. Put each in a different dish. Pour salt on one of them. In half an hour, come back and look at the ice cubes. See what has happened to the one with salt on it.

---

1. You are to find out why icy streets need—
    - **(A) snow**
    - **(B) ice**
    - **(C) salt**

---

2. When you come back, you are to—
    - **(A) taste**
    - **(B) feel**
    - **(C) look**

---

3. You are to put each ice cube in its own—
    - **(A) glass**
    - **(B) dish**
    - **(C) salt**

DIRECTIONS:

Put a check mark after each sentence that is right.

Baby elephants can read. ⎯

We get eggs from hens. ⎯

Rabbits can hop and jump. ⎯

1. You are asked to find sentences that are—
   - **(A) right**
   - **(B) wrong**
   - **(C) funny**

2. You are to make—
   - **(A) circles**
   - **(B) check marks**
   - **(C) lines**

3. Is it right?   **(A) Yes**   **(B) No**

Baby elephants can read. ⎯

We get eggs from hens. ✔

Rabbits can hop and jump. ✔

DIRECTIONS:

Look at the long words and the short words. Find the ones that look most alike. Draw a line between them.

jumped   laugh

walked   jump

laughing   walk

---

1. You are to find words that—
    - **(A) look most alike**
    - **(B) are just the same**
    - **(C) end the same**

---

2. To show the answers, you must—
    - **(A) make lines**
    - **(B) draw circles**
    - **(C) write numbers**

---

3. Is this right?   **(A) Yes**   **(B) No**

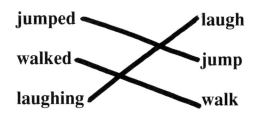

DIRECTIONS:

Do you believe that sound travels better through wood or through air?

EXPERIMENT

Tap your desk. Listen to the sound that it makes. Then place your ear against the desk. Tap again. Now listen to the difference.

1. You are to find out what happens when sound travels through—
    - (A) wood
    - (B) steel
    - (C) walls

2. You are asked to place your ear against your—
    - (A) chest
    - (B) desk
    - (C) table

3. You are to listen for a—
    - (A) difference
    - (B) bird
    - (C) song

DIRECTIONS:

Look at the words in each line. Find a word that does not begin like the other words. Circle it.

bat	face	bee
why	for	find
me	make	get

---

1. You are asked to look at the way words—
      - (A) start
      - (B) end
      - (C) rhyme

---

2. In each line one word must be—
      - (A) circled
      - (B) underlined
      - (C) checked

---

3. Is it right?   (A) Yes   (B) No

bat	(face)	bee
(why)	for	find
me	make	(get)

DIRECTIONS:

Put these words in the right order to make a sentence. On each line, write 1, 2, 3, or 4 to show where the words should go.

to   ___

like   ___

read ___

I   ___

---

1. You are asked to place words in—
   - **(A) a row**
   - **(B) the right order to make a sentence**
   - **(C) the wrong order**

2. To show the right order, you are to write—
   - **(A) check marks**
   - **(B) letters**
   - **(C) numbers**

3. Is it right?   **(A) Yes**   **(B) No**

   to   *3*

   like *2*

   read *4*

   I   *1*

DIRECTIONS:

Read each sentence. Think about what comes first, next, and last. On each line, write 1, 2, or 3 to show the right order.

___ Two friends went into the house.

___ The doorbell rang.

___ A woman opened the door.

---

1. You are to look for the right—
    (A) letter
    (B) word
    (C) order

---

2. To show the right answers, you are to write—
    (A) words
    (B) numbers
    (C) letters

---

3. Is it right?   (A) Yes   (B) No

_1_ Two friends went into the house.

_3_ The doorbell rang.

_2_ A woman opened the door.

A. Exercising Your Skill

A **direction** tells you how to make or do something. There are different kinds of directions. Some directions are the kind you see in workbooks and on tests. Some tell you how to find something out. Some tell you how to put something together. Others tell you how to do something, such as play a game.

Read the sets of directions below. Think about what the directions are for. Match each set of directions with a title from the box. Write the titles on your paper.

```
How to Find Out      Game Directions
        Workbook Directions
```

1. To make new words, add the letter **s** to the end of the words below.
   run _____   walk _____   jump _____

2. Here is how you can find out what will happen to water that is left in a glass. Take a glass of water. Make sure the glass is filled to the very top. Do not touch it again. Look at it in seven days. See what has happened.

3. One person says two words. The other children try to think if the words rhyme. If the words rhyme, the children say **Yes**. If the words do not rhyme, the children say **No**.

B. Expanding Your Skill

Pick a word in a dictionary. Write a set of directions for finding the word. You may not give the page number or tell the word in your directions. Ask a classmate to find the word you picked.

C. Exploring Language

Read each set of directions below. Think about what the directions are for. On your paper, write a title for each set of directions. Your title should tell what the directions are for.

1. Here is how to get to Ted's house. Start at the school door. Turn right and walk two blocks. Turn right again. Count four houses from the corner. That is Ted's house.

2. Here is how to play Mystery Tune. One person hums a song. The others listen. Then they try to guess the name of the song. The first one who guesses will get to hum the next song.

3. You can make a toy for your cat. Put a rubber band through the hole of an empty spool. Tie a small bell at each end. Glue bits of yarn around the spool. Let your cat roll and chase the toy around.

D. Expressing Yourself

Think about something you know how to make. Write directions for making this thing. You may want to draw pictures to go with your directions. Give your directions to someone. See if another person can follow your directions.